Written Remedies

*A collection of inspirational and entertaining
short stories and poems from some of
Scotland's leading authors*

EDITED BY LUCY HEWITT

Luath Press Limited
www.luath.co.uk

First Published 2007 by
Luath Press Ltd.,
543/2 Castlehill,
The Royal Mile,
Edinburgh
EH1 2ND

ISBN (13): 978-1-905222-98-8

The text pages of this book are printed on recycled paper and are
100 per cent recyclable.

Extract from *The Trick is to Keep Breathing* by Janice Galloway is reproduced by
permission of Vintage, Random House.
'How She Came to Write a Poem Called "Apostrophe"' by Dorothy Alexander is
reproduced by permission of Polygon, an imprint of Birlinn Ltd.
'A Simple Thing' by Brian McCabe was first published on the Scottish Arts
Council website.
'A Guid Scots Death', from *Why Don't You Stop Talking* by Jackie Kay,
is reproduced by permission of Picador.
Extract from *Crummy Mummy and Me* by Anne Fine is reproduced by
permission of Puffin Books.

Printed and bound by
RR Donnelley, Edinburgh
B51068 03/07

Typeset in 13 point ITC Charter and Gill Sans by
3btype.com

CONTENTS

A NOTE FROM THE EDITOR

NHSScotland provides free health care at the point of need to the nation. This is an aim which could be said to epitomise the humanity of a society that aspires to be civilised.

For decades it has delivered health care to millions and has touched just about every family in the country at some time in their lives. Through its 150,000 dedicated employees, NHSScotland has created a warmth and affection from patients and service users that is unprecedented for a huge public service.

This perhaps explains the readiness with which the authors who have contributed to this volume gave their support. They are eminent, successful and gifted – they are also busy and in demand; yet each found time to support this unique book.

I am grateful to each of them for their contribution and for their courtesy and encouragement in making this a successful project in honour of a highly respected service.

Lucy Hewitt

FOREWORD

EVERY YEAR I MEET hundreds of the staff who work in the NHS throughout Scotland. It is evident to me that the provision of care by these people is far more than a job, it is a vocation. Whether it is a nurse giving care and comfort to an elderly person suffering dementia, or a physio helping a child recover from an injury; care and devotion like this takes place throughout the service, every minute of every day. The short stories in this book bring all of this to life, and you could become part of it.

NHSScotland employs around 150,000 people – all committed to offering free, high quality health care to everyone in Scotland who needs it, when they need it. Words like *commitment, devotion* and *vocation* are probably used too often nowadays, but when it comes to these staff – they barely do them justice. I can think of no better place to build a career.

NHSScotland offers rewarding careers in over 140 different areas. If you are interested in careers advice then call us on 0845 601 4647, or click on **www.infoscotland.com/nhs**.

Enjoy the stories.

Kevin Woods
Chief Executive, NHSScotland

Extract from

THE TRICK IS TO KEEP BREATHING

Janice Galloway

THE KITCHEN IS BRIGHT, even at this time in the morning. Yellow walls and white woodwork. Inside the white cupboard, a big green box silts at the corners, leaving snuff trails on the floor of the shelf. Family Size Economy Green Label (Strong) Tea. I have no entitlement to a family-size box but it cuts costs: I drink a lot of tea. There is powdered milk in a plastic container shaped like a milkbottle and a white cylinder of saccharine. The cupboard always smells of green label even though there are plenty of other things in there. I once made a list of them and memorised it, just to see if I could. Two tins of soup, dehydrated potato, several jars of beetroot, table jelly, powdered custard, pineapple chunks, packet sauces (cheese and parsley) and the tea things. They all smell of tea. This morning, there's a note as well

Health Visitor 12.30

so I phone school and say I won't come. They never ask why: they're used to it by now.

Friday Morning 10.23

There's a lot to do before she comes but it's a set routine so I don't need to think. It just uses my body and runs itself, hands picking up the cloth and wiping taps after I rinse the emptied cup. I begin cleaning the house.

I can't stop getting frantic about the house being clean and tidy for people coming. I used to watch my mother when I was a teenager and think I'm never going to do that: it's so pointless. I'd tell her things I'd read in books, that my mind was going to be more important than the thickness of the dust on my mantlepiece and she'd zoom the hoover too close to my feet shouting SHIFT to drown me out. I thought I knew something. I looked down my nose at the windolene sheen of my mother's house and knew better while my mother revved the hoover in the background and told me I was a lazy b**ch.

I clean the kitchen till my hands are swollen from cold water, red as ham. My knuckles scrape and go lilac till the kitchen looks like they do on TV and smells of synthetic lemons and wax. I worry about the livingroom. It never looks right. I try not to worry. I try to be grateful since it took me long enough to get here, haggling with tiny-minded Mr Dick from the Housing Authority. Every fourth house in this estate is empty. Kids break the windows and the council have to pay to repair and maintain them empty so the rents go up all the time. Every time the rent goes up more houses become empty, some overnight. But Mr Dick said there were difficulties in my getting tenancy. They have to make a fuss so you know who's boss. There were rent arrears. I wasn't liable but Mr Dick explained if I paid them it might ease the aforementioned difficulties. I said I hadn't got the money.

Mr Dick looked me right in the eye.

Try to be a little more co-operative. We're bending over

backwards. You're not helping yourself, creating difficulties. Strictly speaking, we're under no obligation to house you at all, not when you were never registered as tenant. We needn't do anything at all, strictly speaking. There has to be a bit of give and take. We're bending over backwards you know, bending over backwards.

I said I was sorry about all the trouble they were having on my account and appreciated how good they were being. But I didn't have any money. Surely they understood I had all sorts of debts and expenses at a time like this. Besides the place didn't have a dustbin. Did he expect me to pay for no dustbin?

Mr Dick made his eyes go very small.

There was certainly one there when Mr Fisher became resident, Miss Stone. Oh yes, there was certainly a dustbin on the premises.

His eyes almost disappeared.

I suggest you know more about the whereabouts of this dustbin than you say. And the washing line. Miss Stone.

I paid for the missing things and they gave me back the keys. I got the house.

It's too big really. There are four rooms. One is decorated as a bedroom and the others randomly. There isn't enough furniture to go round. The two armchairs are covered with sheeting. Dust puffs up from underneath when someone sits on them or if they move, really old chairs. The curtains don't meet and are blue. The shelves are his: something to do before we went on holiday. That's why they're not finished. They asked for a receipt to prove the shelves were new, then let me have the benefit of the doubt. His wife didn't want them anyway. The shelves are white, complete enough to house the record player, books, magazines and the phone. The pile of records are mostly his. The Bowie poster hides wine stains where I threw a glass at the wall. A wee accident.

I rearrange things, placing chairs over the bald patches of the rug, sweeping the boards. It never looks as good as I'd like.

By twenty past I'm running along the twisty road between the houses to the shop for biscuits. She likes biscuits. I get different ones each time hoping they are something else she will enjoy. I can't choose in a hurry. I can't be trusted with custard creams so deliberately don't get them. Chocolate digestives are too expensive. I wait for too long in the queue while a confused little kid tries to bargain for his father's cigarettes with the wrong money, so I have to run back clutching fig rolls and iced coffees and nearly drop the milk. I get flustered at these times, but I know I'll manage if I try harder. These visits are good for me. Dr Stead sends this woman out of love. He insisted.

I said, I'm no use with strangers.

He said, But this is different. Health Visitors are trained to cope with that. He said she would know what to do; she would find me out and let me talk. *Make me* talk.

HAH

I'm putting on the kettle, still catching my breath when she comes in without knocking and frightens me. What if I had been saying things about her out loud? I tell her to sit in the livingroom so I can have time to think.

   Tray

       jug

            sweeteners

                  plates

                        cups and saucers

                                    another spoon

                                            christ

the biscuits

the biscuits

I burst the wrap soundlessly and make a tasteful arrangement. I polish her teaspoon on my cardigan band. No teapot. I make it in the cup, using the same bag twice, and take it through as though I've really made it in a pot and just poured it out. Some people are sniffy about tea-bags. It sloshes when I reach to push my hair back from falling in my eyes and I suddenly notice I am still wearing my slippers dammit.

   Never mind. She smiles and says

This is to make out the tea is a surprise though it isn't. She does it every time. We sit opposite each other because that's

the way the chairs are. The chairs cough dust from under

their sheets as she crosses her legs, thinking her way into the part. By the time she's ready to start I'm grinding my teeth back into the gum.

HEALTH VISITOR   So, how are you/ how's life/ what's been happening/ anything interesting to tell me/ what's new?

PATIENT   Oh, fine/ nothing to speak of.

I stir the tea repeatedly. She picks a piece of fluff off her skirt.

HEALTH VISITOR   Work. How are things at work? Coping?

PATIENT   Fine. [Pause] I have trouble getting in on time, but getting better.

I throw her a little difficulty every so often so she feels I'm telling her the truth. I figure this will get rid of her quicker.

HEALTH VISITOR   [Intensifying] But what about the day-to-day? How are you coping?

PATIENT   OK. [Brave Smile] I manage.

HEALTH VISITOR   The house is looking fine.

PATIENT   Thank you. I do my best.

This is overdone. She flicks her eyes up to see and I lower mine. She reaches for a biscuit.

HEALTH VISITOR   These look nice. I like a biscuit with a cup of tea.

We improvise about the biscuits for a while, her hat sliding back as she chews. She doesn't like the tea. Maybe she eats so many biscuits just to get rid of the taste.

HEALTH VISITOR   Aren't you having one? They're very good.

PATIENT   No, thanks. Maybe later. Having lunch soon.

She goes on munching, knowing I don't want her to be here/ that I do want her to be here but I can't talk to her.

This is the fourth time we have played this f*****g game.

The first time was worst. I went through the tea ceremony for five minutes then tried to get the thing opened up.

What are you supposed to come here for? I said.
   She just looked.
   What's it for? What are we supposed to talk about?
   She said, I'm here to help you. To help you try to get better. I'm here to listen.
   But I don't know you from a hole in the wall. I can't do it.
   She said, You can tell me anything you like. I assure you it goes no further and I've heard it all before.

I could hear my own breathing. I knew Dr Stead was doing his best for me and that was why she was here. I had to try. It was reasonable. I swallowed hard. I can't remember what I said now. Whatever it was, I was in mid-flow, keeping my

eyes low because I couldn't look her in the eye. When I finished, nothing happened. I looked up.

She was dunking a gingernut. I watched her hand rocking
back and forth, getting the saturation just right. At the crucial
moment, she flipped the biscuit to her mouth, sucking off
the soaked part, her tongue worming out for a dribble of tea.
It missed. The dribble ran down to her chin and she
coughed, giggling. And I had forgotten what I had to say. I
knew if I opened my mouth something terrible would dribble
out like the tea, gush down the front of my shirt, over her
shoes and cover the carpet like
like
like

She sucked her teeth and leaned closer, whispering.
   She knew how I felt. Did I think doctor hadn't given her
case notes? She knew all about my problems. Did I want her
to tell me a true story? Her niece had an accident on her bike
once. And she thought, what'll happen if Angela dies? what'll
happen? But she prayed to God and the family rallied round
and they saw her through to the other side. That's what I
had to remember. She knew how I felt; she knew exactly
how I felt.

She keeps coming anyway. I make tea and fetch biscuits and
we forget all about that first little hiccup. This time she eats
only the coffee biscuits so I make a mental note. No more fig
rolls. The way I'm coiled is getting uncomfortable. One foot
has gone to sleep and my tea is coated. I put it down on the
rug and straighten up.

HEALTH VISITOR   [Alert to the change] Nothing else to tell
me, then?
PATIENT   No. Nothing special.

She looks blank and vaguely disappointed. I am not trying.

PATIENT   I have a friend visiting tonight. That's all.
HEALTH VISITOR   Anyone special? Going out?
PATIENT   Just the pub, have a few drinks, that kind
of thing.
HEALTH VISITOR   Lucky girl. I can't remember the last time
someone took me out. Lucky.

She smiles and stands up but guilt is spoiling the relief. I get
more guilty as she waddles towards the door, tumbling crumbs
from the folds of blue coat, fastening up one top button,
ready for outside. My temples thunder as she touches the
door and something buzzes in my ear.

You Always Expect Too Much.

The exhaust rattles till she curves out of sight, struggling
against her bulk and the need to turn the wheel.

I rub out the creases on the chairs where we have been sitting then take the crockery through and crash it into the
sink. One of the red cups has a hairline crack along the rim,
fine but deep enough to cut if it wanted. I throw the cup in
the bin in case the person it cuts is not me. I lift the biscuits
still on the plate and crush them between my hands into the
bin. The opened packets follow. They only go soft. The

wrappers crackle with life in the recesses of the liner so I let the lid drop fast and turn on the taps to drown it out. They run too hard and soak the front of my shirt. There isn't time to change. I get my coat and run like hell for the stop.

TO DANCE

Cynthia Rogerson

I USED TO WATCH dancers and say to myself, I am having as much fun watching them dance as they are, dancing. Later, of course, I learned that just isn't true. It is much better to dance. Thank god I learned this in time. I am such a slow learner. My whole life feels like the most agonisingly long waking up.

My wife Martha, on the other hand, is quick and has been 45 – the most capable age – since she was 11. She is 50 now, and shows no sign of doubt yet. Unlike myself, she has always known who she was, what she was capable of. Never treads water, does Martha. And she doesn't know what grey looks like.

Not that black remains black forever and white continually white. No. Once in a blue moon Martha can change her mind, but she puts the whole weight of her belief behind each opinion, as if the opposite view is a mere ball of fluff. She can do this with apparently no recall of what it felt like to hold the previous view. A remarkable achievement, if you ask me, and I admire her immensely.

She has been the backbone of the family. I am older, but I have always felt she is the grown-up and I am allowed certain childlike behaviour provided I go to work every day and wash behind my ears. It is so relaxing having a grown-up for a wife. I rely on her judgement totally.

'What do you think,' showing her the tie I bought.

'No. Won't do. Floral's not you.' Her tone flat, obvious truth needs no embellishment.

But how does she know I'm not floral? Why don't I know?

'Give it to Jamie, he's needing a fancy tie.'

'Is he allowed to go to that do, then?'

'Definitely.'

'But it's £35, just for the dinner. He'll want £50 for the night.' My beer money is £10 a week. I take a packed lunch to work.

'A boy like Jamie needs to feel equal to that lot, meet them on their own turf. He'll not be stopping long here, Harry. Jamie's off places. Give him the tie.'

And the minute her words hit the air, their solid truth is apparent to me. I am not floral. Jamie deserves the do.

So when she announced last week she was going for her annual scan, but it was just routine and absolutely nothing to worry about, none of us did. She drove herself and did the shopping on the way home. I remember she made chicken pie that night, not only because it was delicious and one of my favourites, but because cooking it uses a lot of saucepans and I do the washing up.

I spent an hour that night cleaning the kitchen. Well, there are a lot of us. Six at the minimum, and often more, when the older ones are back from college. They bring their girlfriends and boyfriends home now. I encourage them just as I welcomed all their little playschool and primary school friends. A loud rowdy table full, that's what I like.

Martha's voice rises above it all when things need taking in hand. Only slightly harassed, she'll say 'That'll be enough winding her up, now Calum,' or 'No more of that you lot, or you'll leave the table.' I generally eat silently, or read at the table, if I can get away with it. Noise does not disturb me.

I never even thought to ask her how the scan went. Isn't that awful? But she's been going so long. The lump was 10 years ago, and there's been no recurrence. I had relegated that to the cupboard under the stairs, so to speak. She's had a wee limp the last six months or so, but that was from the time she tripped over the front step.

Yesterday she announced she'd been recalled for another scan. I was surprised. Again, she was not worried, convinced in her dogmatic way it was a mistake and not worth a second of worry. I took her lead as always and buried my worry under some garden work. I did all the hedge trimming and put in the potatoes.

That's something else I've come to learn late. How satisfying it is to see the earth as a fertile skin, to lift out big chunks with a fork, pull out what you don't want – nettles, docks, grass – and resettle with the seeds of what you do want. I used to be intimidated by gardening, feel I couldn't know it. Now I realise it is intensely knowable, whether or not you know the words for things. There is the dirt and there are things growing in it. Almost anything, even a five-foot dock with a root like a parsnip, is ultimately destroyable, and with a little care, almost any plant can grow.

Note the word almost. I do not relish total control. I love to see the grass come up through my gravel path, the rogue poppy seed sprout by the lupins. It reminds me life thrives anywhere, despite complete indifference, sometimes despite intentional discouragement.

I like to think of it all happening – the slow motion changes, the secret lives of worms and beetles, blooms opening or silently dropping off – when I am not there to watch it.

Moonlit nights with only the mice and owls hearing a breeze in the plum trees. I can't explain why, but I find it soothing. A garden is never still, and perhaps most alive when left alone.

Imagine all those lost years before I discovered dancing and gardening.

Today I'm pruning the roses when Martha comes out to tell me the news. It's Saturday afternoon. The doctor has phoned from the hospital. I'm surprised he didn't wait till Monday office hours, like they usually do.

'He said he thinks it's in my bones, Harry. He wants me to come to the hospital now.'

She says this in her normal voice, as if she is saying she has to go to pick up one of the children.

'What else did he say? How sure is he? Do you have to go right now?'

She literally brushes my questions away, like the silly useless noises they are, and turns away to go back in the house.

I try for a minute to act as if the words haven't been said. I finish clipping one scraggly branch off.

An awareness that everything is changing makes me nostalgic. The minutes, hours and days before her words. But that is selfish. I go inside. She is putting some nightgowns in her overnight bag.

'What does it mean Martha?'

'Just what I said.'

'Can they cut it out?'

'Cut out my bones?' with the note of contempt I deserve.

'Well what then. What are they going to do?'

'Where's my slippers?'

'Under the bed. No, in the closet. What can they do to fix it?'

'I don't know. Chemotherapy maybe. Maybe they can keep it at bay for a while. They're not there. Look under the bed for me, will you?'

I kneel and look.

'Here they are. What do you mean "for a while"? What the hell does that mean?'

'Heavens Harry, just what it sounds like.' She clicks her case shut and starts to leave the bedroom. Her back is straight and her step decisive as always.

'Where are the car keys?'

'In the car. Are you going right now? Hold on, Martha, I'll drive you.'

'There's no need. You stay here. I'll phone you when I know anything.'

'But wait a minute, I don't...'

'Dinner's in the freezer, a lamb casserole. Just put it in the oven in about an hour.'

'That's not what I meant. But how long for? In the oven?'

'Two hours. Mind you fetch Ian from the football at six.'

She starts the engine. I am still carrying the secateurs.

'Wait a minute Martha.'

'What is it?' She puts it in reverse and begins the descent down our drive.

'What is going on? Is everything alright?' I feel stupid.

'Everything's fine. I'm going to die soon. I have to talk to the doctor about a few things.'

Then she is looking in the rear view mirror to angle onto the busy road.

But that's my Martha, all the way. First she's completely well and going to die in her sleep at 90, next she's imagining her own funeral and probably making a mental shopping list of what to get for the reception.

I go back into the house, then out again to the shed to put away the secateurs. They hang on a hook up by the window and as I reach my hand up the bright sun shines through it. Momentarily I can see the blood veins and white bones. My skin, which normally looks quite worn and dry is almost transparent. I stop and hold it there and try to see my pulse, the blood coursing through, but of course I can't. Everything inside me is working and unaware of me looking at it. My own body and me feel like acquaintances I should introduce.

Hello hand, this is your owner, who gets a little philosophical about you sometimes.

Oh, is that who you are, well I'm not really interested, says hand, you need me more than I need you.

I am 62 years old. Of course I have thought of dying. I have wondered sometimes that I have not yet succumbed to it. A thousand million cells all specialised, it is so likely some of them will malfunction, so unlikely that I will wake up every morning and yawn as if another miracle has not just occurred. Because not only have all my organs remembered what to do yet again, but the earth, with its layer of top soil holding my potatoes, and all the layers under to the core, have all carried on spinning. At the same time, the very same time that the whole shebang is rotating around the sun. And none of it, not the blood cells or the rocky outcrops, care whether I live or die. So I have lived for some time expecting to die. I also expect Martha to look after me.

I can still hear her voice. I'm going to die soon. She

always knows what to do. How does she know? And does knowing help? Her calm, certain, weary voice.

I leave the shed and get the washing off the line. After I've folded it and laid it in the stacks to be posted to various rooms, I go to the kitchen. I'm doing all this and I'm not thinking of anything. Breathing takes effort. I feel numb and off course. Unreal. The house is empty, they all scatter once they reach 16. I put the kettle on, ignore the baby nettles that have sprouted in the geranium pot on the window sill.

And then I see it on the back of the chair. Martha's bag. At first I think she must be back, be in the house somewhere. She's a creature of habit and she never forgets her bag. It is like a flag flying – I am here and I am taking care of things and everything is fine. Martha unattached to her bag is more earth shaking than her news. Then the phone rings. Her voice is distant and nervous or it may be the connection.

'Harry, is my bag there?'

'It's here. On the chair in the kitchen. You forgot it.' I seem incapable of not sounding stupid.

'Thank goodness. I thought maybe I dropped it in the car park.'

'Are you alright, Martha? What's happening?'

'Nothing yet, I just got here. They've put me in a room and I've got my own phone.'

'I'm coming down.'

'Pick up Ian first.'

'What am I going to tell him?'

'Tell him I'm getting some tests done. Everyone's being lovely here. I'll be home soon.'

'Will you? When?'

'I don't know.' Not words she often says. 'Have you put the casserole in?'

'No. Don't worry about that. Are you sharing the room?'

'No, I'm on my own. There's three empty beds. Guess it's a slack time of year.' A giggle, definitely nervous. 'Come down after eight.'

'Listen, I'm coming down now, Martha. This is stupid. I'll take a taxi and bring the car back.'

'The dinner, the kids...'

'Are not kids any more. They can heat up a pizza.'

'Harold!' She hasn't called me that in years.

'What?'

'Hurry up, then.'

When I began to dance, it was such a relief. But it made me wonder what else I was wrong about.

POEM FOR A HOSPITAL WALL

Diana Hendry

Love has been loitering
down this corridor.
Has been seen
chatting up out-patients,
spinning the wheels of wheelchairs,
fluttering the pulse of the night nurse,
appearing, disguised, as bunch of grapes and a smile,
hiding in dreams,
handing out wings in orthopaedics,
adding a wee drappie
aphrodisiaccy
to every prescription.
No heart is ever by-passed by love.

Love has been loitering
down this corridor.
Is highly infectious.
Mind how you go. If you smile
you might catch it.

ANGER MANAGEMENT

Quintin Jardine

DO YOU EVER GET ANGRY, Neil?' Deputy Chief Constable Bob Skinner asked his friend, as they sat in his garden room, watching the sun go down over the Firth of Forth.

'That's a weird one, out of the blue,' said Detective Superintendent Neil McIlhenney. He took a sip from his diet drink. 'Why do you ask?'

'I dunno what prompted it,' Skinner admitted, draining a little of his Corona beer, through the wedge of lime. 'It occurred to me, out of the blue, that's all. I can't remember ever seeing you blowing your stack. God knows I've gone off the deep end myself, more times than I care to remember. You should know; you've been on the end of it a few times. I've probably got the shortest fuse I know, while you've got the longest.'

'Do I ever get angry?' McIlhenney frowned, staring, unblinking, into the glare reflected by the waters. 'Let me ask you a question instead,' he continued. 'How did you feel when your first wife died in that car crash?'

'When Myra was killed? I was distraught. I was bereft. I was shocked.'

'Is that all?'

It was Skinner's turn to think. 'No, it's not,' he replied when he was ready. 'I was angrier than I've ever been, before or since. I was full of a hot, blazing rage that might have consumed me, if I hadn't had the responsibility of my daughter to keep me on the straight and narrow.'

'So what makes you imagine,' McIlhenney countered, 'that I felt any differently when it happened to me?

'When Olive was diagnosed with her cancer,' he continued, 'at first I was numb, disbelieving. I went through a period of total denial; it was someone else they were talking about, not her, not someone as special as she was, it couldn't be. Then when the truth sank in, and I was forced to accept what the consultant had told us, I got scared.

'The fury followed very soon afterwards. I was angry with God... truth be told I hadn't thought of him much until then, but that made me focus on him, I'll tell you, and give him both barrels. I didn't pray to the so-and-so, I raged at him. But it wasn't just him that copped it. I was angry with the people who made the cigarettes she'd smoked, with the shareholders in the companies, with the farmers who grew the tobacco, and even with the poor sods who harvested it and got paid peanuts, for their part in what was happening to her. I was angry with myself, for knowing the chance she was taking, yet never making any real effort to help her stop. And finally, I was angry with Olive herself, for ignoring all the warnings and for giving herself the disease. That's the part I still find hardest to deal with, that my selfish fury turned on her. That's the part that nearly broke me at the time.'

'But nonetheless,' said Skinner, 'at the time, you kept the rage well bottled up.'

'Yes, I did, because I had to for Olive's sake, and that made it worse.'

'But you stayed in one piece, and you've come out the other side, a better man for it, if I may say so. So what got you through it, apart from your kids?'

'Where's the simple answer to that one?' McIlhenney responded. 'There isn't one, but here's the best I can do. There was a camaraderie about it. We weren't allowed to retreat within ourselves and wait for the end. We found ourselves wrapped in a blanket of caring that enveloped the pair of us, and helped us deal with what was happening.

'Remember Margaret Thatcher?' he exclaimed.

Taken by surprise, Skinner chuckled. 'Who could forget her?'

'Not many, but remember what she said the first time she went into Downing Street as Prime Minister? She had the balls, or the nerve, depending on how you look on her, to borrow from St Francis of Assisi, and part of what she lifted was, "Where there is doubt, may we bring faith. And where there is despair, may we bring hope." I've never forgotten it; and it came back to me during that time; for that's what the people who looked after Olive tried to do, and unlike Maggie, they succeeded.

'They didn't feed us any sugar-coated platitudes, or placebos, and they didn't tell us a single untruth, but from the moment they set out the treatment programme that they recommended, and in the way they communicated it, they gave us faith in them and the certainty that we were in good hands. Once it began, we knew that we were doing something constructive, and the despair we'd felt at the start was replaced by hope. I'm not saying that they took all the fear away, but when we saw that they were never going to give up on Olive, our own determination was made all the greater.'

'But afterwards, Neil,' Skinner murmured, quietly. 'Olive didn't make it. Didn't all the destructive anger come back afterwards?'

'You'd think so, wouldn't you?' said McIlhenney. 'But it didn't; not like it had been. They don't win all the battles. They can't, not yet at any rate. But even when they see they're going to lose one, they stay positive, and they keep you that way. Afterwards, when it's over, along with the bereavement and the shock that you felt when Myra died, and that I did too, there's a feeling of tremendous pride.

'From the moment I met her, I was a wee bit in awe of Olive, and never more so than I was after she'd died, knowing how tremendous she'd been in the last few months of her life. I came to realise that while the disease might have wasted the vessel, nothing could ever kill the spirit that it contained.

'This has nothing to do with religion, Bob; it's my truth. At times such as those, all of us who are left behind find our own certain knowledge, and with it, the peace of mind that lets us go on living. There's a part of St Francis's prayer that Mrs T didn't paraphrase: "Where there is sadness, may we bring joy". To me that's the ultimate, unsurpassable achievement of the health professional. I say this because they helped bring it to me, out of the death of my soulmate.'

'And your anger's gone, has it?'

'Hell, no, it's still there. Its targets are different, that's all. Whenever I see a politician trying to steal a few votes by taking a cheap shot at the National Health Service, that fool incurs my wrath. Whenever I read a newspaper article that attacks it for the sake of selling a few more copies, I want to rip it to shreds and its editor along with it. Whenever I hear of people being denied treatment on the ground of cost alone, by some quango with the power to do it, all the old fury comes back... until in my mind, I hear Olive's voice saying,

"Ignorance warrants pity, Neil, not scorn." That calms me down every time.'

He smiled. 'Don't get me wrong, Bob. I'm not looking at the thing through rose-coloured NHS specs. It's not perfect: I know that. It's a work in progress, and it always will be, has to be. It's got to change, continuously, for when evolution stops, extinction must surely follow. But for the last 60 years it's been a force for good in our country, and if I pray for anything, I pray that it always will be.'

HOW SHE CAME TO WRITE A POEM CALLED 'APOSTROPHE'

Dorothy Alexander

Her friend died and she was heartbroken.

That was in February.

In December, when the chill had really taken hold, there were a few days of spectacular hoar frost, and it was on one of those days, that the first image of the poem hooked itself in.

On the edge of a field in the middle distance, a line of bush-like trees formed a sparkling horizon. There was something about them, held in the powdery air of frost that elicited the first words: trees, cold-powdered, whispered, static. She repeated them as she walked. She wrote them down when she got home.

> *Her friend died and she was heartbroken because it was as if she had come to know some wild but gentle creature that had emerged from the edge of a dark wood; its timidity, its watchful calm bringing out in her a stillness, a desire to be near.*

Isn't it the case when you love something that you never tire of looking at it? Each viewing notes a minute difference, there to be appreciated. She felt this way about the hills of the Tweed valley. It was an easy, accessible feeling. She was driving along the valley south of Innerleithen, wondering how she might feel if she didn't live here, when this line appeared in her head,

'In exile I would write the colours of the hills in winter.' And further along the same road, at a certain bend where it comes very close to the river, the water looked almost still, and that day it had taken on a peculiar colour because of the snow, the shaded position, the trees. She pulled into a layby and scribbled in her notebook, 'the river, eau de nil, in snow, quiet'. She put brackets around 'in snow'.

And she had gained its trust, this vulnerable, shy creature.

One day in January, as she crossed the Lowood bridge near Melrose, she noticed how the low sun shone through an artless, jagged mix of bare deciduous wood and Scots pine. The sky had thickened in the frosty air, fogging the sun: orb, glowing in black trees.

She wrestled with the image, trying to make it exact; it was more an effusion of white mist.

Her friend died and she was heartbroken because she would miss the way her long fingers described the beauty of a thing; the way her limbs moved like a river over stones that would run through her fingers should she try to hold it.

Because from the minute she knew that it was to be death at the end of winter, it was as if the blown light of February had been absorbed, locked into naked trees; as if there could be no synthesis of Spring.

And then it was February again. Sitting on the couch in her upstairs room, she looked out at the sky framed by skeletons of ash and birch, at the undulations of the nearest hills. She sketched the words;

(winter sky),   shades and tones   very bright
low light   fissured   cloud   grey   sage   quiet
   whispering   still
openings of blue, of cream,
the trees don't move, the hills don't move,
trees black and still.

At the bottom of the page she later scribbled an assortment of words that had appealed to her from the dictionary: undersurface, linen-fold, stiffness, apostrophe, mediaeval, and a little reminder of something from the Tao, 'in the Tao there are no separate objects, just differentiations of form within the universe'.

She tried putting together all the fragments and little notes she had made.

As her first line she would take, 'in exile I would write the colours of the hills in winter'. She thought that she might carry on, name the trees, describe the fields, count out the names of farms, villages, towns along the roads of home, a litany of remembrance; poignant. But she was not in exile, therefore she would write of each minute change, each daily, seasonal difference, and the underlying emotion would be quiet joy, something intensely alive and real; the river would flow, she would feel the air, touch and smell the earth.

Because she had held her as she sank forward in bed with her face in her hands and said that she was scared.

But then another voice took over. It began,

> as now in winter the sun appears as an effusion of
> white [she scored out white] mist through black trees,
> a litany of rivers
> exiled in snow
> smooth their patterns to eau de nil
> the sky has written the colours of the hills
> its undersurface of clouds
> shades and tones of bright and low light
> fissured, remembering
> trees hold haze and powder
> whispered static
> earth, stiffness of linen-folds.

It was February, the month she died. It was going to be about grief, remembrance, and how time puts distance between.

> *And since then there had been the doctor's visit. The doctor had told her three weeks at most. She should get her affairs in order.*
> *   This knowledge hung between them now. Her friend was sitting in an armchair. She was wearing a light dressing gown and a pale blue woollen hat because her hair had never grown back after chemotherapy. She was so thin and pale that her face seemed to be disappearing. But she smiled as always... so pleased to see her. Her voice warm as*

ever, just the dry edge of it a bit drier, a bit weaker. Conversation was by the way, she smiled and laughed and when it came time to leave she said that she was welcome anytime.

That this might not be the final farewell was the only thing keeping it all sane. She told her to cuddle into that cashmere. She said her name as they embraced. A last look from the door then out to the car. She felt as if she had left all colour behind, that from now on she would see the world in monochrome. Climbing the steps to her house, she noticed a small group of unopened snowdrops. There was something about their helmet-like heads that was so like hers. Later she wrote a poem with too many adjectives in it.

Ghosted drifts of sleet, your face with the certainty of death in it; an unopened snowdrop filled with ironic laughter, breaking through cold pity to pure white compassion.

She wrote 'lucidity' at the top of the page.

Underneath the last line she wrote:

(hills, fields), engraved, cradled, ghosted, unopened snowdrops, stoic.

The word 'exile' was expanded to give what she knew would be the final line, 'in exile from a time with you in it.' A column of words started to form in the right hand side of the page, 'irony, remembrance, laughter, memory, compassion'. 'Mediaeval' moved into place beneath 'effusion' and 'mist'. 'Apostrophe' moved to the top of the page.

Apostrophe; a mark of elision, denoting something missing.

Because she remembered when they cycled to Gott Bay. It was a day of wind and sun, the air a brisk colour-wash of remembered blues. Dried marram rasped through their wheels but fell silent when they stopped to look at the bay for the first time. 'This is heaven,' her friend had shouted to the wind, and to her. Sand lay like a strip of torn vellum. Great waves rolled and pushed their huge energies.

They had stood and stood; all their looking rhythmed, scoured by wild water. Terns, close above them, shared the unruly wind, held them in their eye. And when she thought about that day it was hard not to see, even in that moment, that fate already had her cast: genre, film noir; soundtrack, waves tearing.

She scored out 'The colours of the hills' and wrote 'compassion' above. 'On' was added to the beginning of the next line. 'Ironic' replaced 'exiled' in the line about snow, and two new lines emerged,

remembering earth; stiff as linen-folds
fissured, engraved with unopened snowdrops.

In the meantime she picked up a Nonesuch Library edition of Donne's poems (she was in the mood for something mournful). She searched for 'A Nocturnall Upon St Lucie's Day'. She sought the grief-laden texture of its cadences. The songs and sonnets were followed by the epigrams and then by the elegies. Elegies; elegy, the word went round and round. She was writing one.

'Elegy', a mourning song, a lament, a serious, pensive poem.

'Elegiac quatrain', four line stanzas, written in iambic pentameter, rhyming abab, classic example Gray's 'Elegy in a Country Churchyard'.

She visited her friend three days before she died. She took some rice pudding… something soft, that she might be tempted to eat. She took a big cashmere scarf that her grandmother had knitted. She took a card that had a painting of frilled cream-coloured tulips against a pale blue ground on the front. Inside the card she wrote how much she appreciated her as a friend and that she loved her. Opposite this she inscribed a short poem by Raymond Carver, written when he was dying of cancer. It was called 'Late Fragment'.

*And did you get what you
wanted from this life even so,
Yes I did.
And what did you want?
To call myself beloved,
To feel myself beloved on the earth.*

She took a fresh piece of paper. Apostrophe, title. Elegy written in the top right hand corner.

She counted out the syllables of the pentameter. They looked like this:

As now in winter the sun appears through
black boughs, effusion, mist, mediaeval.
A litany of rivers, ironic
in snow, smooth their patterns to eau de nil.

She was amazed.

> The sky writes compassion on the underside
> of clouds, in shades of bright – light,
> remembering earth stiff as linen-folds,
> fissured, engraved with unopened snowdrops.

This would need some work, and the last stanza would have only two lines.

> Trees held in haze and powder; whispered static,
> in exile from a time with you in it.

But they scanned. They half-rhymed.

She was so pleased. It looked as if it would work as a form of elegy. She deliberately did not want to force it into the classic form. She wanted to be aware of it, acknowledge the rules but break them to give a lighter, more modern feel.

In the second stanza she changed the third line to 'remembering earth's stiffness as linen-folds', 'remembering' now given only three syllables. Another small column of words began to appear in the bottom right hand margin: former, previous, ancient, old, golden, lapse, something missing, absent, predecessors, lineage, forbears. A circle was whirled around 'lapse'. Sounding 'ps', it took its place at the end of the line. Then, as if from nowhere, the word 'oblivious' arrived and the second line was rewritten thus; 'of clouds, oblivious to bright or lapse'. And that was it. She checked it over: syllables, rhyme and half-rhyme, the chiming of the short 'a's; the long 'o's; the short 'i's; the incidental rhyming of first and third line end words in the first two stanzas with other words in the second and fourth lines of each; not too many adjectives, and those that were there were working hard.

Her husband read it. 'Fissured is a favourite word of yours.'

She stared and stared at the offending word. She pen-cilled in 'fractured', although 'fissured' was not scored out. Two days later 'fractured' was inserted. It gave another short 'a', it kept the sense, enhanced it even, gave it a harder feel, and chimed with the hard 'c's of ironic, compassion, static. She scribbled out 'the' before 'underside' and changed it to 'undersides'. Her husband didn't like this. That was his favourite line, just the way it was. Back to elision.

And when she wrote in a poem that she wore her grief as a shroud of spilt colours, she could hear her friend reminding her that the pigment of their lives was as inde-terminate as the blue of the sky.

APOSTROPHE

As now in winter the sun appears through
black boughs, effusion, mist, mediaeval;
a litany of rivers, ironic
in snow, smooth their patterns to eau de nil.

The sky writes compassion on the underside
of clouds, oblivious to bright or lapse,
remembering earth's stiffness as linen-folds,
fractured, engraved with unopened snowdrops.

Trees hold haze and powder; whispered; static;
in exile from a time with you in it.

WHAT MATTERED ABOUT THE DANCING

Carol McKay

WHAT MATTERED ABOUT the dancing was the liberating spontaneity of unplanned movement. Hand on her partner's shoulder, all Greta had to do was hold him as he steered her round the dance floor. And holding him was effortless. She was past the quick breath intake she'd felt the first time she'd submitted to Nathan's gentle pressure urging her backwards. Now it was her weekly dose of exuberant physicality, her quintessential sensory satisfaction. Better than the brief tongued gloss of melting chocolate. Better than the olfactory tease of breakfast's bacon sweetened with tea. Her occupational therapist had been so right to suggest it.

Give her the 32 cold stone steps of the staircase reverberating with Mrs Matheson's purposeful *Greensleeves;* the film of damp from the close wall under her fingertips; her breathless arrival at the second floor to warm sunlight on her shoulders and Nathan's voice above the music, louder as she twisted the creaking door knob and entered the hall. Her cane tap-tapping like a metronome, anticipation at a plateau as the music stopped and little girls flurried around her to change.

She would slip off her shoes and coat to calls of 'next week' and the bumping of the door, the rumble of Mrs Matheson's piano stool and the aroma of coffee. Then Nathan's measured foot fall would approach across the sprung floor.

'Greta, darling, you look radiant. Purple suits you.'

She'd rise, hand reaching for his touch.

What did it matter that the little girls whispered he was

gay? That he wore a pink striped leotard over a strip-waxed chest? What mattered was the timbre of his voice, the firm muscle of his shoulder, the soft brush of his eyebrow pierced by its beaded pin, and the warm oil of the crease in the hollow of his eyes.

As he led her, free of her cane, free of her caution, what mattered was Mrs Matheson's opening chord on the piano and Nathan's muscular body tight against her. It didn't matter that she couldn't see him. What mattered was the wide, empty dance floor, and this long-forgotten freedom of movement. She owed this happiness to her therapist! What mattered was that Nathan was taking her *dancing*.

A SIMPLE THING

Brian McCabe

HE COULDN'T GET TO SLEEP, partly because old Norman, in one of the beds across from him, was having a bad night. Although he'd partially drawn the curtain round his own bed to shut out the light from the night nurses' station, he could still see the old man's head rolling from side to side as he groaned 'Oh Jesus Christ' repeatedly into his oxygen mask, then muttered a lot of other things he couldn't make out. A couple of nurses had been to see Norman once already since lights-out and they'd given him a pill, but it didn't seem to be having any effect. He hoped they'd come back to check on him again soon.

It didn't seem to bother Mattie, who was in the other bed opposite: he was snoring like a tractor, as usual.

He took a drink of water and rearranged his pillow. He still found it difficult to sleep every night, although he'd been in the same bed now for over a week. The ward was L-shaped and he was lucky to have one of the three beds on the bottom of the L, tucked around the corner, so most of the noises he heard during the night came from Norman and Mattie. On the other hand, the bottom of the 'L' was nearest the door to the ward, so anyone coming or going walked past his bed. It was the busiest part of the ward during the day. He could also sometimes hear the night nurses at their station just around the corner, talking to each other in low voices, chattering and giggling, but if anything he found this reassuring. It was strange to watch these young girls dedicating their time to looking after old men like Norman. It was the contrast that seemed strange – young, lively, healthy girls in their 20s and exhausted, wrecked old men who ranged between 60 and 80. Of course, he was in the ward too, but at 51 he was the exception.

Mattie was an exception of a different kind: he must be in his mid-60s, but he was still a well-built man with an intact sense of humour. His rugged features had sagged, but he'd obviously been handsome in his youth. He was always joking around, sometimes putting a cardboard potty on his head to do a song-and-dance routine for one or other of the nurses who came round in the mornings and evenings with the medication trolley.

The other day he'd heard a consultant, who'd obviously got to know Mattie well over the years, saying, 'You'll never learn, will you? I keep telling you: just go on the way you are, if you want to die!'

Mattie had responded: 'Well I'll die happy then, a whisky in one hand, a fag in the other!'

The first morning he'd woken up in the ward, unaware that he'd been brought here from Intensive Care while asleep, Mattie had come over and sat on the end of his bed. 'How's the new kid?' he'd said.

'Where is this?'

'Well, it's no the Afterlife – yet. What you in for, young man like you?'

'I just... had a heart attack.'

'*Just* a heart attack? Is that all? Well, that's OK then! Join the club, son. That's what it is, it's a club. Once you're in here, you can guarantee you'll just keep coming back!'

He'd felt too exhausted to explain that he meant *just* in the sense of 'recent' and Mattie was already telling him about all the operations he'd had, almost as if he was proud of them, concluding with: 'Double-bypass, triple-bypass, the works. My chest's like the railway map of Scotland.'

Old Norman had quietened down a bit, though his head was still rolling from side to side on the pillow and every so often he pushed aside his oxygen mask to let out a long rasping breath, half cough and half wheeze. It didn't sound quite human; more like the protest of a defective industrial fan.

He thought about calling a nurse and asking for a sleeping pill himself, but felt that he was already pumped so full of chemicals that he didn't really want to add to the cocktail. Maybe that was a sign of fighting back, a first step towards reclaiming normal life. He'd had the angioplasty two days ago and today for the first time he was able to get out of bed and walk to the toilet, helped by a nurse. It was such a simple thing, but it felt like a personal victory. Tomorrow morning, the nurses had said they would remove the dressing in his groin where the wound was, where the hollow needle had been inserted, then the wire and the balloon-tipped catheter to inflate the artery before putting the stent in place. It had been weird to watch it all happening on a screen as they were doing it: the wire slowly moving up the artery which looked like one wild branch of a forking tree of lightning. It had been difficult to remember that this was going on inside him as he watched – the shot of morphine they'd given him had kicked in, making him feel even more removed from it all.

Stitching the wound after the procedure, the young Australian doctor had said to him: 'That's it, mate. We've done our bit. Now you do yours.' By which he meant stop smoking, change your diet, change your lifestyle, take exercise. It was daunting to think about what he would have to do and what he would have to not do, but the alarm in his youngest daughter's wide blue eyes when she'd first visited him in Intensive Care and had seen him wearing an oxygen mask had stayed with him. It was an image of what he himself felt: he was too young for this to be happening to him. But when the dressing was removed, he might be able to have a shower, then he might start dressing himself in the morning rather than staying in his pyjamas. Again these were such simple things, but he longed for them.

The heart attack had put other things into a different perspective too. When he thought about his job on the paper now, meeting deadlines every day, sometimes several a day, phoning up people to interview them, checking his facts and his sources, checking his e-mail every five minutes, writing the copy at high speed, subbing it, getting it in to be typeset for the next morning's paper... And the lifestyle that went with the work – the hour or two in the pub after work, the drinking and the smoking and all the shop-talk with his colleagues, the gossip and the nasty jokes, the competition for column inches, for a pay-increase, for promotion, for awards... It was as if he was suddenly watching himself taking part in these things from above, from a remote spot he had somehow landed in, and it looked like a form of frenetic insect life.

Though worried about his job and who would fill in for him, he was glad that the consultant had told him he'd have to take a few weeks off. The things he missed and found himself longing to get back to were simple things too: going for a drive down the coast and having a walk by the shore with his wife, calling in somewhere on the way home for a glass of wine. Shooting the breeze with his friends in the pub. Taking his teenage daughters to their dance classes on Saturdays, joking around with them in the car and hearing their laughter. Having a meal around the table, a meal he or his wife had cooked – maybe it would be the Moroccan Tagine she sometimes made or that stir-fried prawn thing he sometimes attempted with chillies and basil and garlic... Thinking about food was making him feel hungry and that would make it even more difficult to sleep. Even so, he couldn't help anticipating the bowl of cereal, the toast and tea he'd get for breakfast. He tried to put it out of his mind but felt his stomach shrink and pucker in a mute plea. If he couldn't sleep during the night, he would probably fall asleep during the day and miss the mid-afternoon tea and biscuit. This had happened to him twice already, and he'd felt absurdly upset. It wasn't that the tea was so great – in fact, he'd taken a tip from Mattie and asked his wife to bring in some better teabags – but when you were lying in bed all day and doing very little, that cup of tea became an event of considerable importance. And he didn't want to be found asleep in bed when his wife and kids came to visit; he wanted to be up and in his dressing-gown, reading the paper... No, not the paper – he couldn't face that. He'd make it a book.

The previous evening he'd watched Mattie larking around just before visiting hour, wearing the earphones from his radio and doing a parody of a flamenco dancer, taking one of the flowers from the vase on his bedside table and putting it between his teeth. He'd grabbed hold of a nurse – a very pretty girl who happened to be Spanish – and she'd laughed and gone along with it for a minute or two, raising her slender arms and clapping her hands and stamping her feet and crying out a guttural *Ay!* before telling him to behave himself and get ready for his visitors.

'Right enough, I better get into bed and look pathetic.' And he'd done just that, lying splayed in his bed and groaning in a parody of the helpless invalid.

Before his own wife and daughters had arrived, he'd watched Mattie's extensive family gather around his bed. They were a lively bunch, talking to each other as much as to him, though they crowded round him and gave him lots of attention. He watched a boy of about eight years old – almost certainly one of Mattie's grandchildren. Unable to get near enough Mattie himself because of all the others, the boy had kissed the edge of the bed instead. Mattie was loved; he had much to live for.

Old Norman had had only one visitor that he'd seen. A woman in her mid-50s, very thin and birdlike with her spiky brown hair and restless movements. It was probably his daughter. Although she fussed around the old man, adjust-ing his pyjamas and his oxygen mask and the objects on his bedside chest, it was clear that she didn't really know what to say to him any more, and most of the time Norman was either so exhausted with the battle to keep on going or was so blurred by his medication that he barely responded to her questions.

Mattie's snoring hat settled into an even uphill-and-downhill, see-saw rhythm and it might be possible to fall asleep now except that Norman had become more agitated again. 'Oh

Jesus Christ, no!' he kept repeating, more clearly now because he had either pushed the oxygen mask off his face or it had been knocked aside. The muttering was also louder, clearer: '... no right, no mysel, no mysel the night, there's somethin far wrong...'

When he leaned forward to peer through the gloom of the ward he could see the old man's body heaving in the bed and his head thrashing from side to side on the pillow.

He reached up and pressed the button to call a nurse, then he pressed it again.

They were there in an instant. The curtain was drawn round the bed, but there was a light of some kind behind the curtain, so that he could see the shadows of the nurses moving around on the curtain. They were talking to the old man, asking him questions, trying to get him to respond, but he just kept on groaning 'Jesus Christ!' and muttering other stuff he couldn't make out. After a few minutes the doctor arrived, then a small trolley with electronic equipment of some kind was wheeled into the ward and taken to the bedside.

There was no point in trying to sleep with all this going on. He sat up in bed and swung his legs out from under the covers. He reached for his dressing-gown and draped it round himself without putting his arms into the arms, then he stood up and pushed the curtain around his bed aside. He needed to go to the toilet, but couldn't ask one of the nurses to take him at the moment. Anyway, he had to try it on his own some time. He walked very slowly, trying not to put too much weight on his right leg. He felt like leaning on something, but didn't really want to hold on to the ends of people's beds. By the time he had walked the length of the ward to the toilets, he was ready to sit down. He peed first, holding on to the hand-rail on the wall and leaning his whole weight on his left leg. When he had finished he put the lid down and swung his body round to sit down. He pulled down his pyjama trousers enough to look at the dressing. It was dark with dried blood, and yellowing at the edges. He prised it from his skin slowly until he held it in his hand. The darkened, hardened underside looked like the underbelly of a crab, with its damaged legs of surgical tape splaying out at the sides. He opened the small bin by the side of the sink and threw it in.

There was a box of tissues on top of the cistern. He plucked a few of the tissues out, turned on the hot tap and dribbled a little water over the tissues. Then he cleaned the wound. He repeated the process a few times, until it was as clean as he could make it. His groin was swollen and yellowed with bruising, but it would get better in time. He stood up and opened the window, then sat back down on the toilet seat. The night air came in, and he could hear traffic pass on the other side of the park. He felt for the packet of 10 and the lighter, which were still hidden in his dressing gown pocket. He'd transferred them from the pocket of his jeans earlier in the day, while no one was looking. There was one cigarette left. He took it out, smoked half of it, then ran it under the tap to put it out. After a week without, those few draws made him feel dizzy, queasy, so he sat for a few minutes more before closing the window and flushing the toilet. He unlocked the door and walked slowly back along the ward, until a nurse – it was the Spanish one Mattie had flamencoed with – interrupted her phone call to come from behind the desk at the station and stopped him with an outspread hand. He thought he was rumbled, that she knew exactly what he'd been doing in the toilet, but all she said was, 'Please. You must wait one moment there? Thank you.'

She went back to the phone call. He sat on the edge of her desk – his legs felt weak and his groin had started to throb – and waited. He could hear the voices just around the corner, then the ward doors being opened. The squeaky wheels of a trolley. When the nurse hung up, she walked to the corner of the ward, looked around it, then motioned for him to come.

As he turned the corner, he saw that they'd taken Norman away. The curtain had been pulled to the side, exposing the empty bed. He climbed back into his own bed one leg at a time, taking care not to move too quickly or bump his groin against anything. He looked over to Mattie, who was now sitting up in bed and staring straight ahead.

'Mattie?'

Mattie took a while to look over to him.

'What happened? Did they take him to Intensive Care? What's wrong with him?'

'Nothing's wrong with him, son.' he said. 'He's deid.' Mattie turned to face the wall and pulled his covers up around his neck. 'Better try to sleep now son,' he said.

Extract from

THE BLUE MOON BOOK

Anne MacLeod

WEEKS ARE PASSING, days flying. Mornings have grown darker, evenings too. Jess doesn't notice. Her leg is still in plaster. She's walking now, managing the crutches. It's taken a while for her to get the hang of them.

At first, when she came round, life had been difficult, lacking shape, lacking organisation. Things are gradually assuming relevance, importance. Not that she thinks of it in that way. Not that she thinks of it at all.

Watching her from the door of the four-bedded ward, Sian notes considerable physical improvement. Jess is sitting up, beginning to take notice, and if she still has the slightly dazed expression of the newly awake, at least she is watching, listening. There's an element of euphoria too, none of the frustration you'd normally predict in someone denied speech who had used words creatively, lived by them. It is almost as if Jess has no need to communicate, feels happy enough surfing the relative calm of the ward. This isn't good enough. Sian wants to see greater recovery than this. She hopes they can achieve it. Only on the one occasion has she witnessed Jess striving to reach beyond immediate comfort.

Yesterday the tree outside the ward window, a rowan, had been filled with finches, snub-nosed, orange-breasted, stripping branch after branch of their shockingly red berries. Jess watched, fascinated, hobbled across the ward to the window. Tried to open it. It was too stiff, and perhaps, thought Sian, perhaps the catch was a little complicated for Jess's damaged fingers. She could not shift it, turned in panic, searching, caught Sian's eyes.

'No,' she said. 'No. No.'

She still had only the one word, though the range of expression she imbued it with was growing.

Sian had smiled. 'We can't open that window, Jess. It's stuck.'

'No.'

'I think they keep them locked for insurance purposes.'

Sian wasn't sure about that, but it sounded plausible. She sat down, began to run through exercises designed to enable automatic speech, but Jess would not pay attention, kept following the birds. The berries were all gone by the end of the session.

Finches were nothing if not efficient.

Today Jess's attention is not on the outdoors. She's staring across the ward. The other three patients sit together, chatting, not consciously excluding Jess, but not including her.

'Hi Jess!'

Sian waves. Jess, does not turn, does not respond. Sian knows there is no problem with her hearing.

'Hello, Jess!' Louder. 'Hello, Jess!' Louder still.

This time Jess turns, but not with recognition, more in non-specific response to noise, any noise. Sian smiles, waves again. Jess looks. Does not wave. Are the corners of her lips dancing slightly? Sian wonders if they are. Broadens her own smile. Perhaps this is, after all, a beginning.

'Excuse me.'

'Sorry.'

Sian steps back to let the female ambulance driver pass. Ah. This must be the girl who visits Jess. What's her name? Janet? She's heard about Janet, hasn't had the luck to catch her yet. The most regular visitor, according to the nurses, and the one Jess seems happiest to see. Sian has wanted to meet her. Now, she stands at the door, watching unobtrusively.

'Hi there, Jess.' The green-clad girl smiles, perching on the bed. 'And how are things?'

'No,' says Jess.

'That good?'

'No.'

'Hmm. My day's been a bit like that.' Janet reaches into her breast pocket. 'Brought us a Caramel Log. Fancy one?'

'No.'

'Good. Here you go.' She tosses the brightly wrapped biscuit to Jess, begins unwrapping her own. 'I don't like sweet things usually,' she says. 'But I really go for these. Don't you?'

Jess is having trouble with the wrapping. The skin on the fingers of her right hand is still raw. The damage was extensive, and has been slow to heal, infection after infection in the grafted areas. Janet sits waiting, patient, does not offer help. Jess gets there slowly, holding the biscuit in her right hand, painstakingly and clumsily peeling with her left. Janet does not begin her own biscuit till Jess's is unwrapped.

'Guess what, Jess?'

Jess raises her head smartly.

'Want to hear the latest?'

'No.'

Sian is struck by the conversational tone, by the natural body language Jess is using.

'Kev and me. It's all on.'

'No.'

'Yes. We went Salsa dancing last night.'

'No.'

'It's not so much dancing as sex with clothes on.'

Janet bites into her Caramel Log. Jess looks at her. Sian is watching very carefully. Jess looks at Janet. Jess looks at Janet, almost smiles. Takes the initiative.

'No?' Her voice is bright with mischief, keen with question.

Janet grins. 'None of your business!'

The afternoon light has veered from autumn to winter, sun slanting low across a changeable city sky. That would never be a summer blue, thinks Sian, calling her thoughts to order, bringing her attention to bear on the room, on the patient. She is trying to encourage Jess to vocalise, trying to persuade her to make any sound but No. She's having little success. Perhaps it's simply too late in the day. Jess will not co-operate, keeps allowing her attention to wander, her gaze to drift. Sian tries a new tack.

'Ella was telling me you had two visitors this afternoon, even though Dan's away. Ken and Janet.'

'No.'

'Did they come together?'

'No.'

Sian knows they didn't.

'And how was Janet? Was she f i n e?' Sian stretches the word out, repeating the question.

'How was Janet? F.. i ..?'

'No,' says Jess.

There's much less variation in the quality of communication in that single syllable than Sian heard in the earlier conversation with Janet.

Sian tries again.

'Nice to have a friend to visit. How was Janet? F.. i ..?'

'No,' says Jess.

'And Ken?' Sian moves on, shaking her head. 'Is Ken fine too?'

Jess's face, till now lacking in any expression but the startled openness of Barbie dolls or beauty contestants, suddenly looks sad. Almost definitely sad. Almost definitely frustrated.

And she laughed at Janet too, Sian remembers.

Interested, Sian pushes Jess, just a little; keeps talking about Ken. She's come to like him. Knows the gossip, of course. The recent divorce. Much of the hospital sympathy (for what that's worth) has run with him.

'What are you trying to tell me, Jess? Something about Ken?'

'No.'

'We can do it in simple words. One word if you like. You can tell a one word story. We've talked about that, haven't we? What's Ken's story? Happy?'

'No.' Jess sighs.

'Sad?'

'No.'

'Chocolate biscuits?' Sian offers a distraction here, suggesting Janet's visit.

'No.'

'Dancing?'

Jess nods. 'No. No.'

'You are fond of Ken, aren't you? Y.. e.. S?'

Jess says nothing. Sian is still trying.

'And Janet, you're fond of her. Aren't you? Y.. Y..'

'Eh.' The sound is so small Sian can hardly hear it.

'Good, Jess. That's really good. That's another word! That's magic, Jess. *Another word.* That's so great! Well done! Try it again? Yy..'

'Eh..'

Sian feels like hugging her. Fights to control her obvious emotion, keep her own voice steady. 'That's so great, Jess.'

She is greatly moved, unable to say anything more for several seconds. She smiles. Jess smiles too, blushes, fiddles with the paper on her trolley. Silence stretches between them, stretches till a young auxiliary nurse darts into the ward, her broad smile trained on Jess.

'Jess! A postcard for you. See? It's only just come in the internal mail – went to another ward this morning. And it's been round the whole of Scotland, look at it – redirected *four* times! It's a wonder it ever got here!'

All three bend their heads over the scrap of card, an image against blue sky of an ancient standing stone carved with intricately woven birds, wings and beaks enmeshed.

'Wow,' says Sian, finding her voice at last. 'Let me read it for you, Jess. Would you like that? Yy..'

'Eh.'

Sian turns the card over, squinting at the postmark. The place of posting is illegible, the date a little clearer. It has somehow taken weeks to reach the ward.

'*Good to meet you. Keep in touch. Michael.*' She hands it back. 'That's all. Who's Michael?'

'No.'

Jess stares at the picture, lost in the interwoven intricacies of the design. The Michael who sent it gets short shrift, little attention. The picture, though, that moves her.

She seems, Sian sighs, to have frozen out so much of her life, set it in amber. The memory loss preferentially disrupting interest in people, in relationships. Ward staff have found it difficult explaining that to friends and colleagues, all so sure *they*'d be remembered, all so hurt, offended, when they were not.

'You look tired,' she says. 'I'll come back later. Bye for now. Bb..'

'No,' says Jess.

'I know.' Sian smiles. 'You're tired.' She stands up, patting Jess's shoulder. 'I'm proud of you. That's a big, big step you've taken today.'

Dan

The sun had swept so low, street level was in deep shade. Dan found it difficult to choose the right key for the door as he swept down with bags and boxes of food to the hired car. Living on the fourth floor had had its effect. He was fitter. Lighter. He was glad to finish here though, glad to be leaving. Glad he had his licence back.

He smiled a little as he humped the very last suitcase down the last flight of stairs. He'd been up and down these steps a dozen times and met no-one. This did not surprise him. He'd been in this building months and never met anyone on the stairs, not once. Other folk did live here at night; you could hear their radios, their television sets. They seemed to be invisible.

A flat near the Tron had sounded a good idea; central, certainly. But traffic noise roared late into the night, invasive without double glazing. Triple-glazing might, he thought, actually be necessary. Even that might not keep out the yells and shrieks that shattered the night's peace, the indecipherable shouts of joy or panic, drunkenness, fighting; all the irregular clamour of a city centre. It had never been possible to get a full night's sleep, even in the first weeks, even in that binge. Now he'd taken a new flat in a genteel terrace in Merchiston. It should be a great deal quieter. He'd like to let the house in White Street go... once he was able to discuss it with Jess. once he could be sure she understood what he was saying.

These had been the loneliest weeks of his whole life. Drifting every day from the cold and noisy flat to the hospital where Jess no longer screamed, but would not notice him. He knew she could communicate, after a fashion, with the nurses. He'd seen her nodding at the staff, shaking her head. He'd even heard the odd automatic word. No. She never spoke to him. Would not respond to him. When he came near, she assumed.. no, be more precise.. her face assumed... a fixed expression, closed. It was as if she could not bear to see him, did not want him near. As if she thought he might be going to hurt her.

'It's a post-traumatic thing,' Sian, the young speech therapist assured him. 'Not something she's able to control. Not something we can really help her with until her language and other communication skills improve.'

'That's not a comfort.'

'No.'

Sian didn't lie. He liked that.

On this occasion she turned to him and said, 'You'll have to dig deep, rely on all that strength I know is in you, Mr

McKie. Jess is going to need support. An infinity of it. You're all she has.'

Dan almost broke down then, almost confessed to Sian how imperfect the relationship had been.

'I expect,' she went on, 'you're thinking that you're only human, that life wasn't perfect anyway before the accident. Or maybe you were different. Maybe you and Jess had that unusual thing, a good relationship.'

'Not exactly,' said Dan, thinking how distancing that *Mr McKie* was. She was always formal with him. She called Jess *Jess*.

'We all have our cross to bear.'

Not you, thought Dan. Your life must be so clear. Uncomplicated.

Sian was still speaking.

'Life's rarely straightforward. What is simple and obvious is that Jess is going to need months, perhaps years, of self-less support. Are you up to that?'

'I think,' said Dan slowly, 'I'd need support myself.'

'That's what we're here for,' Sian nodded. 'That's exactly what we're here for. Counselling would help too, help you through all the frustration.'

He hadn't been sleeping well. The street noise didn't help, but it had surprised him how often he found himself thinking about Sian. Her measuring stare seemed challenging, addictive. It reminded him of someone. She was, perhaps, a little like his sister Grace? And not unlike Jess.

Well, that was the flat clear. He pushed the keys, as directed, in the caretaker's letter box. He'd never once seen the caretaker. Presumably one did exist. This was a surreal world, this empty city tenement, rented out to visitors. It must be visitors. No-one else would find it easy to survive here. What you could put up with for a week is one thing, what you needed for daily life another.

He took himself for one last stroll down the High Street. It had been his habit to walk from the flat to Holyrood and back each night. There was always something happening. There was always the chance of meeting Sian.

He knew her flat. He'd known that since the first evening; which close she lived up, which square. He'd seen her at her window. It did no-one any harm, walking these quiet streets at night. Exercise was beneficial. Got him away from the whisky, from the silent phone. From the TV.

That *Mr McKie* was very distancing.

It was what she called him even when they met outside the hospital.

Even when, like tonight, he was strolling down the street lost in thought and didn't recognise her till she was almost past. Why would he? It was Halloween. Scurries of tiny witches and warlocks clogging the pavements. Death-heads, Munch-white *Scream*-heads wavering in and through the shadows, laden with plastic carriers, these bulging white supermarket bags at odds with the funereal costumes. Halloween had changed. It used to be enough to wear your sister's coat, your mother's headscarf. A football strip. He's seen himself do that.

Avoiding two miniature Harry Potters, he stumbled into two girls, arm-in-arm, swinging out of a close.

'Sorry.'

He would have walked right on, but one of them stopped, reaching towards him.

'Mr McKie,' she said. 'Hello. I thought you were moving.'

'I am,' agreed Dan. 'I'm just getting a bit of air before I go.' His gaze switched from Sian to her taller friend.

'Let me introduce my twin, Jamie. Jamie, this is Dan McKie.'

Jamie stretched out a hand. 'Hi there.'

She was taller than Sian, taller than Dan. Red hair hung to her shoulders, dancing over them. She looked to have a great deal of humour, but she was not at all like Sian. Not like a sister, never mind a twin.

'Good to meet you,' Jamie grinned.

She knows, thought Dan. *She knows.*

'Hope the move goes well,' Sian smiled. 'We'll be thinking of you.'

'Och, it'll be fine. The new place will be quieter. I'll get more sleep. Well,' he hovered awkwardly, 'I ought to be off.'

'See you next week.'

'Aye.'

He sauntered on. Did not look back until he was a good three, four blocks down. They'd crossed the road, still arm-in-arm. Women, thought Dan. That touch, that warmth. By the time he was making his way back up the hill, they were no longer in sight. He walked, head slightly bowed, into the drizzling dark.

Jess

'Here's your chocolate, Jess,' the young nurse slaps the mug down on the bedside table, spilling brown sweet liquid everywhere. It floods the melamine top, lapping the postcard Jess has been staring at.

'No!' There's real distress in Jess's voice. 'No!'

'What is it, Jess?'

Jess holds up the card. 'No.'

'I'm sorry. Look, give me your towel. Give me your towel, Jess,' the nurse asks, 'Hurry, before the stuff sinks in.'

Jess reacts quickly. Stretches across the bed and throws the nurse her face cloth.

'That'll do. There you are.. well done! You'd hardly know now, would you.. it's the quality of paper they use nowadays. Jess!' the girl stops, amazed. 'You gave me the right thing. Nearly the right thing. Look, Jess.. your towel.. *look*. L. L..'

'–ook,' Jess finishes the word.

'Jess! That's another word! Another w.. W..'

'.. orr,' finishes Jess, staring at the postcard, tracing the birds' interlocking beaks, following the intricacy of their ornate wings.

The girl, who's been watching Sian at work, races off to the nurse in charge. Jess goes on caressing the birds.

'Look,' she says. 'Look.'

When the staff nurse comes Jess waves the postcard at her. 'Look.'

'Very good,' the staff nurse says. 'Very good. But don't forget your chocolate. Don't want you losing sleep, do we?'

She looks carefully at the card. 'The words are still there. Look, it says *keep in touch,* see? And who's Michael? Is he nice?'

'No,' shrugs Jess, slipping the postcard into her drawer

and picking up the dripping mug. She wipes the bottom of it on her face cloth before she drinks.

'No.'

A GUID SCOTS DEATH

Jackie Kay

KEN THIS: YOU'RE BORN; you live; you die. It comes doon to this. The cost of ferrying you from hospital to parlour to crematorium. Forget the future. Forget it. You're no making it to next year. Your skin is hinging off. All this talk aboot time all the time. I've had it up tae here.

I'm trying to remember what I was told about my own birth. Ten a hauf pounds. Midnight. My maw screaming for God. It doesnie mean onything. Even your own life, it turns oot, doesnie mean dickie bird. Your ain habits and likes and dislikes. Puff! and away they go. A wee show of stars and then the big, biding dark. Looking back tae this and furward tae that. It's no real so it's no.

I'll tell you what's real. Dying. I feel mysell relishing it. Folk are listening tae what I'm saying like my words are gold. Hinging on my every pronouncement. I cannae shout ma words anymair. Thur whispered oot. My voice is dimmin doon noo. So they're leaning, sinking, faces close, close. They could be inside me. I'm this close tae them. My own death – this close. Right up agin them. Close as a breath intae the oxygen mask and back again roon my own chin. I'll no be forgotten. I will be forgotten. No, I'll no be forgotten.

I'll no see my Japanese jugs ever again. Or my wee sheltered hoose. But by Christ, I've lived a life and a hauf; I've made it tae my age, wi' all my bits and my ain hips and nae plastic in me at all. And that's mair than I can say for some folk a lot younger! But I'm no looking as young as I could because I lost my teeth. I don't know where I put them. They're either in my hoose or in the ambulance. I dinny like people to see my gums. It looks that ill tae see, an auld woman wi' a sunk chin, dribbling.

Here I um. I've got an oxygen mask on my face that puts me in mind o' my rain hats. Pulled the string tight under my chin tae keep my hair nice. What a sicht in the rain. Oxygen masks on ma heid and bright red lipstick.

I'm running doon the High Street wi' a wean in each haund and I'm full of violence. My ain violence is snatching my breath. I stop and tug Pearl's brown coat, back and forth. She's girnie and crabbit and she's at it and she knows it. I've had it. I skelps her right oot in the street. None of this namby pamby, 'Whit do you think?' stuff that's making a mess of today's children. It's a guy dreich day and oor Pearl's hair is soaking wet and the rain is pouring doon my face and I cannae tell if it's the rain or tears pouring doon Pearl's. Bruce is smiling a sly smile that maddens me so I cuff him across his heid and tell him he's next. And he hings, lanky aroon the lamp-post, heid doon, scowling. And here the two of them are at my bedside. And I don't know if they're crying fir the past or crying fir me.

I've always had my opinions. There's folk that are empty-heided and when you ask them whit they think aboot such and such, they look glaikit and say, 'I'm no sure.' Nae fibre in them. Nae *All Bran*. Noo that I'm sitting right next to the big High Heid yin himsell, Mister Death, I find I've still got things tae say. Things I want said. I'm no feart aboot going. When I go, a lot goes with me. I know that because my kind are no made anymore. Everyone's that saft and full of excuses noo. Nae backbone.

I've always been a fussy wuman. Just like the wee robin that comes tae visit my sheltered hoose. The robin is an affy fussy bird. Same spot, same bit of the wall, every year. I'd gie it a bit o' the fat from my ham, it wouldnie take bread. My granddaughter brought some lavender oil and put it on my flannel; I had tae tell her tae get it aff. It was sickly sweet, an awful hippy smell like yon patchouli they flower folk used tae wear wi' their long hair. Nearly made me boke. I dinny like sweetness. I cannae trust sweetness. Whit is there to be sweet aboot? I dinny like a sweet smile, all sugary. I like a good soor smile. A smile that says, 'I kin still manage a wee smile despite all the horrific things that have been happening to me.' I like plain. I like soor. Gie me a soor ploom, a bitter lemon or a squeezed lime straight on to my tongue. Gie me a man wi' a long soor face so I ken where I um. I dinny like they men that trick you into thinking you could be happy, the ones wi' pressed sharp trousers and shiny shoes, dancing with long slow smiles.

My hands are all wired up noo. God knows what all is going intae me. Stuff fir my heart, my liver, my blood pressure. Drips tae stap me dehydrating. My haunds are covered in bruises all over. I dinny ken whaur they're going tae find tae put any mair needles in. I'm like the bionic woman there's that many wires in me. My hands have never shirked. I dinny even haud back from the needle.

I was work; work was me. I couldnie stop. Your whole body felt the work in you, nagging and goading your veins. I was fit. My airms had muscles like a big muckle man's. My back would be that sair from the hard work. Making yir fist tight, bloodless, scrubbing and rubbing hard. Right doon on your bare knees. It was like fighting – work. Yir anger came oot in ragged breaths till you'd rubbed it up guid. Roon an roon an roon an roon an roon. Pit a shine on it. Made it shriek wi' cleanliness. My elbows were working elbows, dry skin on them. My sleeves always rolled up for my bucket so they did-nae get wet. Whit was a cut or a scrape tae me? By Christ, they don't ken work now. They don't ken heid and horn that feeling in your body when yir body has been taen over, when yir body belongs to work. But then I came hame, stane-tired and wabbit and they hudnie done whit I asked them to do. The dishes werenie touched. The floor wisnae swept. They'd feel it then, the back o' my haund.

And here they are at my bedside, Pearl and Bruce, the baith of them wi' too much beef on them. Bruce wi' his baw face and wan o' they beer bellies. Pearl's still got a bonny face but her smile is a fossil through whirls and rolls o' fat. And here's me: never put on an extra pound in my puff. Never wasted a single meal. Here's me – skin and bone. My haunds all papery and wistful hauding my children's thick, big fingers. You dinny get used tae yir child's haund getting big. It feels wrang forever. I'd say tae them, when they were wee, gie me yir haundie and I liked the feeling o' it, the wee, innocent han' in my ain. Weel. Thur no innocent noo. Some-times, I have tae pull my haund away because I still cannae staund to be touched for too lang. All my words have run oot and are dribbling doon my chin.

There's been plenty folk to see me. Lovely flowers. Cards. Folk leaving, greetin'. I can manage a wave wi' my wired hand like an old puppet. One of the men from The Rowans gave me a hug, leaning right over the hospital bed. I says, 'That's the first grope fray a man in 17 years.'

We never talked aboot sex. No the way they do today. Oh my God. We didnae have the words for hauf o' what went on. We just did it in the dark. Lights oot and then the fierce fumbling. Wance, I gave oot a long slow moan, like bagpipes fillin' wi air – nyuuuuuuuuuuuuuuuuuuuur – fir I was quite enjoying it and my man sat bolt upright, snapped the light on, and cries, 'Whit's wrang wi' you? He thoucht I wis having a heart attack. This wis aboot the last time I had sex. I was nearly 60. I didnae miss it that much. No that I can remember noo.

I've left my hoose neat. My pants are all folded in my drawers. My blouses are all thegither in the wardrobe. My nighties are all clean. I've got 50 skirts she'll hae to give to charity. I've got plenty towels and flannels and god knows all what. I've aye been neat. I wis even a neat walker. I wisnae wan o' they clumsy wuman, ill-hung-thegither, gangly and ungainly, getting in everybody's way. I've got sma' feet. My feet have always been nice. Nice toes, the lot. Thur no coming apart wi' corns and bunions and dry skin. My bones are coming through now. My working bones. There's no going to be bones like this in the future. By Christ, no.

There's no a thing wrang wi' me except the auld heart's packed in. But them years younger have got illnesses I've never heard of. I think they make the names up. Jist the other day I wis hearing people noo believe men kin get post-natal depression. Well tae hell wi' that. People sad aboot the rain and the winter. People eating hail packets o' chocolate biscuits jist tae throw them up again. Folk that cannae eat a raspberry wi'oot their tongue swelling oot and throttling them. Royals having thur jobbies irrigated. Folk wi multiple personalities when one's enough. People wi M.E. Me me me. They're welcome tae it. I'm gled I'm jumping ship. Nae plastic hip fir me. Nae pacemaker. No walking stick. No blood pressure pills. No hearing aid.

I'd rather have somebody shout straight into my lug than wear a hearing aid. They don't look nice. They look like they could be alive, they strange pink things, like foetus in folks' ears. There's them that embrace the stick and the zimmer, that cannae wait tae get auld and stoop their back and moan and complain and curry favours.

The wan thing I conceded to wis false teeth. I couldnie o' managed wi'oot them. And noo I'm up a closie where I cannae find ma teeth. And I've no looked so auld in my life. I dinny want tae die wi'oot my teeth, bit nae teeth, nae teeth. Whit does it mean dying like this wi'oot your teeth? Wull it bring me bad luck. We used tae say if a bairn wis born with teeth, it was dreidfae unlucky. That bairn could grow up tae be a murderer. Auld wives' tales. Where will the auld wives go noo?

Auld wives like me. They'll drop the auld wives and the tales. And whit will they be left with? Sleaze and violence. The world is upside doon. It doesnie make any sense. There's no one to say dinny. Dinny, naw, because how else are the weans tae learn? The bairns today are indulged; their parents are feart o' them. It used to be the ither way aroon. But naw! Now the slightest whine and it's a poke o' sweets. Parents have tae bribe their kids tae get them to put on their claes. Oh Jesus. They are welcome tae it. The hale wurld is spinning oot o' control. The earth's boiling; you cannae eat the beef; there's folk still starving. But the fat sow's arse is always greased.

The auld wives are leaving time. Their long skirts and

long faces that stood at the gate and watched whilst their man wis brought hame drunk on the back o' a coal cart. The auld wives that gossiped and blethered to create a toon. The wans that knew the men wuid let them doon. The men wuid drink the blood of the family. The blood wis drained from the auld wives' cheeks; the auld wives were peely-wally. And there wis the man, his cheeks a ruddy red, blood enough for all of them.

It's the auld wives lowsin time. The wans that never cried or foutered, scuttered or shied away from the truth. The auld wives that waved at the fishing boats and put on a brave face. The bonnie fechters, the wabsters weaving, plashing and plaiting. The auld wives that made sure a fresh loaf was brought intae the hoose in the new year. The wans that kept their bread bins clean for their mother-in-laws. The auld wives that never threw ashes oot on New Year's Day, feart o' throwing ashes in thur saviour's face. The auld wives that lit and blew oot the candles. The thrifty auld wives, the mourning auld wives, the credulous auld wives. The fish wives, the biddies, the weedows, the guid wives, the hens that rabbit on, all of them will be gone, gone. The auld wives that opened the doors tae let the auld year oot. They are going; they are going at Hogmanay. The wans wi' the grim, worked faces, the scarves over their heids. The wifies singing the auld songs since auld lang syne. *How can ye bloom sae fresh and fair? How can ye chant, ye little birds, And I sae weary fu' o care.* The loops and the looms and the landscapes lost, the banks and braes, the singers, the songs, the poems by heart, going, going. The auld wives are going awa', airm in airm away from the future.

Alang the ward, the char lady comes with a cup of tea I cannae drink. I dinny want food noo. I dinny want onything. All I want is a cold hand on my forehead, a cold flannel pressed into my skull. I want Pearl to pit water on her fingers and rub my tongue. All day lang, the nurses walk up and doon the corridors in thur uniforms.

This wire going intae my airm is thinning my blood. This wan is diamorphine. It will kill me in the end. This one is regulating my kidneys. This wan is taking oot ma urine. I'll never sit on a toilet seat again. The nurses are doing that much fir me. They are never away from me. All my wires, my drips, my bruises.

My oxygen mask keeps falling doon my face. The elastic at that back o' my heid isnae tight enough. But these young nurses will never become auld wives. Wance you've had the auld roond once, they don't come the same again. Neither do the weans. These young nurses have got my life in their hands and they're gentle wi' it.

My sight still sees. But everything else is getting weaker and weaker. I feel I could just slowly fade away till nothing wis left o' me but my skin and bone, lying on the hospital sheets. Along the corridor, I can see them coming, Pearl and Bruce, their faces all strained. It's as if they are saying to me, they cannae take any mair o' it. Pearl's got a strange wee smile on her face the day. She sits doon at the side o' my bed and rustles in her handbag. And oot comes my teeth. 'Dunaaaa!' says she, wi' a flourish.

'In the name of God,' I says to Pearl, 'Whaur did you find them?'

'They were at the back of the drawer in your mahogany

dresser behind all your purses,' she says. I sit up and shout, 'nurse, nurse, it's a miracle. Pearl's found my teeth.' And the nurse comes. I try and fit the teeth intae my mooth. It takes me the longest time fir my gums are too dry fir teeth. 'Noo,' I say to the wee pretty nurse, 'whit dae you think of me? Dae I look glamorous? At least I'll no be all gums for my leaving.' I say and Pearl squeezes my wired haund and greets, 'Oh Mum!' And dabs at her een. She looks at me as if she's proud o' me dying like this. 'Did you no ken yir mother had so much panache?' I says winking at Pearl. Bruce greets as well, silent-like. Mind, he always wis a greetin-Teenie.

I pu my teeth oot o' my mouth and lie them at the side, on tap o' the hospital cabinet. I fancy thur smiling at me, they teeth of mine. Pearl pulls my rain hat back over my heid and all I can hear is the sound of my own breath, going in, oot, in, oot, in, oot. Ye ken, it sounds like the sea, me. I sound like the sea. Haaaaaaaaah. Haaaaaaaah. Awa. Awa. Awa.

Extract from

CRUMMY MUMMY AND ME

Anne Fine

YOU DON'T EXACTLY *ask* to get sick, do you? I mean, you don't go round *inviting* germs and viruses to move in and do their worst to your body. You don't actually *apply* for trembling legs and feeling shivery, and a head that's had a miniature steel band practising for a carnival in it all night.

And if you should happen to mention to your own mother that you feel absolutely terrible, you would expect a bit of sympathy, wouldn't you?

I wouldn't. Not any more.

'You don't *look* very poorly.'

That's what she said. And she said it suspiciously, too, as if I was one of those people who's always making excuses to stay off school and spend the day wrapped in a downie on the sofa watching *Teletubbies* and *Playschool* and *Lunch with Andy and Puts*.

'Well, I feel absolutely rotten.'

'You don't look it.'

'I'm sorry!' I snapped. (I was getting pretty cross.) 'Sorry I can't imagine a bright-green face for you! Or purple spots on my belly! Or all my hair falling out! But I feel rotten just the same!'

And I burst into tears.

(Now that's not like me.)

'Now that's not like you,' said Mum, sounding sympathetic at last. 'You must be a little bit off today.'

'I am not *off*,' I snarled through my tears. 'I'm not leftover milk. Or rotten fish.'

'There, there,' Mum soothed. 'Don't fret, Minna. Don't get upset. You just hop straight back up those stairs like a good poppet, and in a minute I'll bring something nice up on a tray, and you can have a quiet day in bed with Mum looking after you until you feel better.'

That was a bit more like it, as I think you'll agree. So I stopped snivelling and went back to bed. I didn't exactly hop straight back up those stairs because I was feeling so crummy and weak I could barely drag myself up hanging on to the banisters; but I got up somehow, and put on my dressing-gown and buttoned it right up to the top to keep my chest warm, and plumped up my pillows so I could sit comfortably, and switched on my little plastic frog reading lamp, and folded my hands in my lap, and I waited.

And I waited.

And I waited.

(In case you're wondering, I was waiting for Mum to bring me up something nice on a tray and look after me until I felt better.)

She never came.

Oh, I'm sure that she *meant* to come. I'm sure she had every intention of coming. I'm sure it wasn't her fault the milkman came and needed paying, and it took time to work out what she owed because he'd been away for two weeks on his holiday in Torremolinos.

And I'm sure it wasn't Mum's fault that he took the opportunity to park his crate of bottles down on the doorstep and tell her all about the way some sneaky people always bagged the best pool-loungers by creeping down at dead of night and dropping their swimming towels over them; and how his wife's knees burned and peeled but none of the rest of her did, even though all of her was out in the sun for the same amount of time; and how his daughter Meryl came home to her job at the Halifax with a broken heart because of some fellow called Miguel Angel Arqueso Perez de Vega, who'd danced like a fury but turned out to be engaged to a Spanish girl working in Barcelona.

Oh, it wasn't Mum's fault that she had to listen to all that before she could get away to bring me up something nice on a tray and look after me until I was better. But I could hear them talking clearly enough on the doorstep. And I don't actually recall hearing her say firmly but politely: 'Excuse me, Mr Hooper, but Minna's in bed feeling terrible, and I must get back upstairs, so I'll listen to all the rest tomorrow.' I heard quite a bit, but I didn't hear that.

As soon as the milkman had chinked off next door, I thought I heard Mum making for the bottom of the stairs. But she never got there.

'YeeeeooooowwwwwaaaaaAAAAAAAAAAAEEEEEEWWW!'

You guessed it. Crummy Dummy woke up.

And I suppose it wasn't Mum's fault that Crummy Dummy needed her nappy changing. And that there weren't any dry ones because we don't have a tumble-drier and it had been raining for three solid days. And Crusher Maggot had forgotten to pick up a packet of disposable nappies before he went off to Sheffield for a few days to help the sister of a mate change flats.

So Mum decided the simplest thing would be to park Crummy Dummy in the playpen where little accidents don't matter. It wasn't her fault it took forever to drag it out of the cupboard because Crusher had dumped some great heavy lump of car innards right in front of it. Or that she had to fetch the damp nappies off the line and drape them over the rack in the kitchen.

And I suppose it's understandable that while she was shaking out the damp nappies, she should glance out of the window at the grey skies and think about nipping down to the launderette with the rest of the washing and handing it to Mrs Hajee to do in the machines, since it really didn't look as if it would ever stop raining.

So I suppose it does make sense that the very next thing I heard on my quiet day in bed was Mum bellowing up the stairs:

'Minna! *Minna!* Look after the baby for a few minutes, will you, while I nip down to the launderette? She's perfectly happy in her playpen with her toys. Just come down if she starts to squawk.'

To be fair to Mum, she didn't stay out any longer than was absolutely necessary. There was the launderette, of course. And then she had to get the disposable nappies or Crummy Dummy would have had to spend the whole morning sitting on her cold bottom in the playpen, waiting for the ones in the kitchen to dry. And while she was in the supermarket she did pick up bread, and a quarter of sliced ham, and a few oranges and a couple of other things, making too many to get through the quick check-out. And there were really long queues at all the others because it was pension-day morning. And she did just pop into the newsagent's on her way home as well. And, yes, she did stop on the corner for a second, but that was just to be polite to the Lollipop Lady who told her that, whatever it was I'd got, there was a lot of it about, and Mum ought to be really careful or she'd come down with it as well.

And then she came straight home. She *says* she was out for no more than five minutes at the very most. But I've a watch, so I know better.

Then, at last, she came up to my room. She had Crummy Dummy tucked under one arm, all bare bottom and wriggles, and she was carrying a tray really high in the air, practically above her head, so Crummy Dummy couldn't upset it with all her flailing arms and legs. It was so high I couldn't see what was on it from the bed.

'I don't know how these nurses do it,' said Mum. 'They should have medals pinned on their chests, not watches.'

I looked at mine. It was exactly half past ten. (I fell sick at 8.23.)

'If you were a nurse,' I said, 'you would have got the sack two hours ago.'

'I'd like to see you do any better,' she snapped back, sharpish.

'I bet I would,' I told her. 'I bet if *you* were sick, it wouldn't take *me* two whole hours to bring you something nice on a tray.'

'I should wait till you see what there is on the tray before you start grumbling,' Mum warned. And then she lowered it on to the bed in front of me.

And there was a cup of very milky coffee with bubbles on top in my favourite fat china bear mug, and a huge orange cut into the thinnest possible circular slices, just how I like it when I want to nibble at the peel as well. And a chocolate-biscuit bar and the latest *Beano* and *Dandy,* and a pack of 20 brand-new fine-tipped felt pens.

I felt dead guilty for being so grumpy.

'I'm sorry I said you'd get the sack as a nurse.'

'Oh that's all right,' Mum answered cheerfully. She flipped Crummy Dummy over and put a nappy on her before there was trouble and even more laundry. 'It's a well-known fact that it's even harder to be a good patient than a good nurse.'

'Is that true?'

'Certainly.'

And then, with Crummy Dummy safe at last, Mum sat down on my bed and took a break.

I thought about what she said quite a lot while I was getting better. As I sipped my coffee, and nibbled my orange circles, and read my *Beano,* and made my chocolate biscuit last as long as I could while I was drawing with my brand-new felt pens, I wondered what sort of patient Mum would make. She isn't famous in this house for long suffering meekness or sunny patience.

And I wondered what sort of nurse I'd make – sensitive, deft, unflappable, efficient...

I'd no idea I would find out so soon.

It was only two days later, on Saturday morning, that Mum leaned over the banisters and called down:

'Minna, I feel just awful. Awful.'

'You don't *look* very poorly.'

(I didn't mean it that way, it just popped out.)

You'd have thought I was trying to suggest she was faking.

'I may not *look* it, but I *am*,' she snapped. 'I feel as if I've been left out all night in the rain, and my bones have gone soggy, and hundreds of spiteful little men with steel boots are holding a stamping competition in my brain.'

Personally, even without the Lollipop Lady saying there was a lot of it about, I would have recognised the symptoms at once.

I was determined to show Mum what proper nursing ought to be.

'You go straight back to bed,' I ordered. 'I'll take care of you, and everything else. You tuck yourself in comfortably, and I'll bring up something nice on a tray.'

Mum swayed a little against the banisters. She did look pale.

'You are an angel, Minna,' she said faintly. And wrapping her shiny black skull-and-crossbones dressing gown more closely around her string vest nightie, she staggered back into the bedroom.

I don't have to tell you about my plan, do I? You'll already have guessed. Yes, I was going to rush back into the kitchen and spread a tray with lovely, tempting treats for an invalid's breakfast – treats like a cup of tea made just the way Mum really likes it, golden-pale, not that thick, murky, dark sludge favoured by Crusher. (He says Mum's tea is too weak to crawl out of the pot.)

And I was going to pick a tiny posy of flowers from my half of the garden, and arrange them in one of the pretty china egg cups.

And I was going to bring the tray up without delay.

Guess what went wrong first. No, don't bother. I'll tell you. First, I locked myself out. Honestly, me, Minna. The only one in the house who *never* does it. I did it. I was so keen to get my tray arranged that I stepped out of the back door into the garden to find the flowers without checking the latch.

Clunk!

The moment I heard the door close behind me, I realised. I could have kicked myself in the shins. I picked my way around to the front, just on the off-chance that the front door was unlocked. But I knew it wouldn't be, and of course it wasn't.

I stood there, thinking. I had two choices. I could ring the doorbell and drag poor, shaking, deathly-pale Mum from her bed of sickness and down the stairs to let me in; or I could slip next door to old Mrs Pitopoulos, ring her bell instead, and ask to borrow the spare key to our house she keeps for emergencies in an old cocoa tin under her sink.

I knew which a good nurse would do. I went next door and rang the bell.

No answer.

I rang again.

Still no answer.

Suddenly I noticed a faint scrabbling overhead. I looked up, and there was Mrs Pitopoulos in her quilted dressing-gown, fighting the stiff window-catch with her arthritic fingers.

She couldn't budge it, so she just beckoned me inside the house.

I tried the front door. It was locked. I went round the back, and that door opened. I picked my way through the furry sea of all her pet cats rubbing their arched backs against my legs, so pleased to see me, and went upstairs.

Mrs Pitopoulos was sitting on the edge of her bed. Her face looked like a wrinkled sack, and her wig was all crooked.

'You look very poorly,' I told her.

I couldn't help it. It just popped out.

'Oh, Minna,' she said. 'I feel terrible, terrible. My legs are rubber, and there are red-hot nails in my head.'

'I've had that,' I said. 'Mum's got it now. The Lollipop Lady says that there's lots of it about.'

When she heard this, Mrs Pitopoulos began to look distinctly better. Maybe when you're that age and you get sick you think whatever it is has come to get you. At any rate, she tugged her wig round on her head, and even the wrinkles seemed to flatten out a bit.

'Minna,' she said. 'Would you do me a great favour, and feed my hungry cats?'

'What about you?' I said. 'Have you had anything this morning?'

'Oh, I'm not hungry,' Mrs Pitopoulos declared. But then she cocked her head on one side, and wondered about it. And then she added:

'Maybe I do feel just a little bit peckish. Yesterday my sister brought me all these lovely things: new-laid brown speckled eggs and home-made bread and a tiny pot of fresh strawberry jam. But what I'd really like is...' (her eyes were gleaming, and she looked miles better.) 'What I'd really like is a bowl of Heinz tomato soup with bits of white bread floating on top.'

Even I can cook that.

And so I did. And fed her cats. And she was so pleased when I brought the soup up to her on a tray that she pressed on me all the little gifts her sister had brought round the day before: the new-laid brown speckled eggs and home-made bread and tiny pot of fresh strawberry jam – oh, and the door key of course.

Mum was astonished when I brought the tray up. I thought she must have been asleep. She looked as if she had been dozing. She heaved herself upright against the pillows, and I laid the tray down on her knees.

'Minna!' she cried. 'Oh, how lovely! Look at the flowers!'

You'd think someone who claims to like flowers so much would take a little bit more care with her half of the garden, wouldn't you?

'Wait till you've tasted the food,' I said.

I could tell that she didn't really feel much like eating. But she was determined not to hurt my feelings, so she reached out and took one of the strips of hot buttered toast made from the home-made bread.

She nibbled the crust politely.

'Delicious,' she said. And then, 'Mmmm. *Delicious.*'

She couldn't help dipping the next strip of toast into the new-laid brown speckled soft-boiled egg.

'Mmmm!' she cried. 'This is *wonderful.*'

After the egg was eaten, she still had two strips of toast left. She spread one with the fresh strawberry jam, and off she went again.

'Mmmm! *Marvellous!*'

She went into raptures over the golden-pale tea. I reckoned poor old Crusher would have a battle getting her back on the thick, murky, dark sludge when he came home. And then she leaned back against the pillows, smiling.

She looked a lot better.

'I'll bring you some more, if you'd like it,' I offered.

'You are the *very best nurse*,' Mum declared. 'You managed all this, and so quickly too!'

Now I was sure she'd been dozing. I'd taken *ages*. '*You're the very best patient*,' I returned the compliment. 'You don't notice what's going on, or how long it takes!'

'Silly,' she said, and snuggled back under the bedcovers.

I think she must have thought I was joking.

NOTES ON THE AUTHORS

JANICE GALLOWAY is the author of seven books of prose, prose-poetry and poems. Her first novel, *The Trick is to Keep Breathing*, now widely regarded as a Scottish contemporary classic, was published in 1990. *Foreign Parts, Blood, Where You Find It*, and *Clara*, a novel based on the life of 19th century pianist Clara Wieck Schumann, also received wide critical acclaim. Her most recent book, *Rosengarten* (with sculptor Anne Bevan) explored obstetric implements. She is currently working on a new novel, has one son and one husband, and lives in Lanarkshire.

CYNTHIA ROGERSON'S first novel, *Upstairs in the Tent*, was published in 2000, and her second, *Love Letters from my Deathbed*, was published in 2007. Her poems and short stories have appeared in anthologies and literary magazines, as well as being shortlisted in competitions and broadcast on the BBC. She is Californian and has lived in Scotland for 30 years.

DIANA HENDRY has published three poetry collections, *Making Blue, Borderers* and *Twelve Lilts: Psalms and Responses*, plus *Sparks!* with Tom Pow. Now living in Edinburgh, she has worked as a journalist, a creative writing tutor at the University of Bristol and as Writer in Residence at Dumfries & Galloway Royal Infirmary. She also writes short stories and has published more than 30 books for children, including *Harvey Angell* which won a Whitbread Award in 1991. She has also published a collection of poems for children, *No Homework Tomorrow*.

QUINTIN JARDINE is married with an extended family of four adult kids, and two Tonkinese cats. The rarely reclusive author can normally be found in the Mallard Hotel, Gullane, East Lothian, or in Trattoria La Clota, L'Escala, Spain. Having spent the first part of his working life trying, with moderate success, to persuade journalists to accept his version of the truth about politicians and PR clients, Quintin Jardine took to crime writing both naturally and with relief.

DOROTHY ALEXANDER is from the Scottish Borders. She has just completed a PhD in Creative Writing at the University of Glasgow (for which a novel with poems about a group of Alzheimer's sufferers titled *Cage* was written), and is now working on a part-fiction memoir that will include a re-telling of the story of the Mauricewood Pit Disaster. Married with two children, she previously worked as a nurse. 'How She Came to Write a Poem Called "Apostrophe" ' won the Macallan/ *Scotland on Sunday* Short Story Competition in 2002.

CAROL MCKAY'S short fiction has appeared in *Chapman, Mslexia, The Herald* and in the Polygon anthology *Shorts 5.* She's also a regular contributor to the showcase at **www. clydevalley.net.** Carol's now working on a fast-paced novel, *Incunabula*, in which a woman searches for family in a male-dominated post-apocalyptic setting. In her day job, Carol teaches creative writing through the Open University and gives readings and workshops through the Scottish Book Trust's Live Literature Scotland scheme. Her website is **www. carolmckay.co.uk**.

BRIAN MCCABE, born in a small mining community near Edinburgh, studied Philosophy and English Literature at

Edinburgh University, to which he was appointed Writer in Residence in 2005. His latest poetry collection is *Body Parts* (1999). His most recent volume of short stories, *A Date with My Wife*, was published in 2001, and his *Selected Stories* in 2003.

ANNE MACLEOD lives on the Black Isle with her husband and four children. She studied medicine in Aberdeen and now works as a dermatologist. Her poetry and fiction have been widely published and her first novel *The Dark Ship* was nominated for the Saltire and IMPAC awards. *The Blue Moon Book* is her second novel.

JACKIE KAY was born in Edinburgh in 1961 and grew up in Glasgow. *The Adoption Papers* (poetry) won the Saltire and Forward Prize. *Other Lovers* (poetry) won the Somerset Maugham Award and her first novel, *Trumpet*, won the Author's Club First Novel Award and *The Guardian* Fiction Prize. She lives in Manchester with her son.

ANNE FINE has been an acknowledged top author in the children's book world since her first book was published. She has won every major award, including the Carnegie Medal (twice), the Whitbread Children's Novel Award (twice) and *The Guardian* Children's Literature Award. She has twice been voted Children's Writer of the Year at the British Book Awards and was the Children's Laureate from 2001 to 2003. She has written over 40 books for young people, including *Goggle-Eyes, Flour Babies, Madame Doubtfire* and *Road of Bones*, and her books have been translated into more than 25 languages. She has also written a number of acclaimed adult novels.

Luath Press Limited
committed to publishing well written books worth reading

LUATH PRESS takes its name from Robert Burns, whose little collie Luath (*Gael.,* swift or nimble) tripped up Jean Armour at a wedding and gave him the chance to speak to the woman who was to be his wife and the abiding love of his life. Burns called one of 'The Twa Dogs' Luath after Cuchullin's hunting dog in *Ossian's Fingal*. Luath Press was established in 1981 in the heart of Burns country, and now resides a few steps up the road from Burns' first lodgings on Edinburgh's Royal Mile.
Luath offers you distinctive writing with a hint of unexpected pleasures.

Most bookshops in the UK, the US, Canada, Australia, New Zealand and parts of Europe either carry our books in stock or can order them for you. To order direct from us, please send a £sterling cheque, postal order, international money order or your credit card details (number, address of cardholder and expiry date) to us at the address below. Please add post and packing as follows: UK – £1.00 per delivery address; overseas surface mail – £2.50 per delivery address; overseas airmail – £3.50 for the first book to each delivery address, plus £1.00 for each additional book by airmail to the same address. If your order is a gift, we will happily enclose your card or message at no extra charge.

Luath Press Limited
543/2 Castlehill
The Royal Mile
Edinburgh EH1 2ND
Scotland
Telephone: 0131 225 4326 (24 hours)
Fax: 0131 225 4324
email: sales@luath.co.uk
Website: www.luath.co.uk